Tenor Saxophone

The

Christopher Norton

Concert Collection for Tenor Saxophone

15 original pieces
for tenor saxophone and piano

BOOSEY&HAWKES

Boosey & Hawkes Music Publishers Ltd
www.boosey.com

Published by Boosey & Hawkes Music Publishers Ltd
Aldwych House
71–91 Aldwych
London
WC2B 4HN

www.boosey.com

ISMN 979-0-060-12626-0
ISBN 978-0-85162-879-0

First impression 2013

Printed in England by The Halstan Printing Group Ltd, Amersham, Bucks

www.christophernorton.com

CONTENTS

American folk tunes

1. Turkey in the straw 2

2. Swanee river 3

3. Polly Wolly Doodle 4

4. Carry me back 5

5. Dixie 6

Christmas

6. King Boogie 7

7. We wish 8

8. Good Christian men 9

9. Camel stomp 11

10. I saw three ships 12

Nursery rhymes

11. Put it all together 14

12. Hush little baby 16

13. Twinkle 17

14. Black sheep of the family 19

15. Kettle rag 20

1. TURKEY IN THE STRAW

Christopher Norton

2. SWANEE RIVER

Christopher Norton

3. POLLY WOLLY DOODLE

Christopher Norton

4. CARRY ME BACK

Christopher Norton

6

5. DIXIE

Christopher Norton

6. KING BOOGIE

Christopher Norton

7. WE WISH

Christopher Norton

8. GOOD CHRISTIAN MEN

Christopher Norton

BLANK

PIANO

The
Christopher Norton

Concert
Collection
for
Tenor Saxophone

15 original pieces
for tenor saxophone and piano

Boosey & Hawkes

Boosey & Hawkes Music Publishers Ltd
www.boosey.com

Published by Boosey & Hawkes Music Publishers Ltd
Aldwych House
71–91 Aldwych
London
WC2B 4HN

www.boosey.com

© Copyright 2013 by Boosey & Hawkes Music Publishers Ltd

ISMN 979-0-060-12626-0
ISBN 978-0-85162-879-0

First impression 2013

Printed in England by The Halstan Printing Group Ltd, Amersham, Bucks

www.christophernorton.com

CONTENTS

American folk tunes

1. Turkey in the straw 2

2. Swanee river 5

3. Polly Wolly Doodle 8

4. Carry me back 10

5. Dixie 13

Christmas

6. King Boogie 15

7. We wish 17

8. Good Christian men 19

9. Camel stomp 21

10. I saw three ships 24

Nursery rhymes

11. Put it all together 27

12. Hush little baby 30

13. Twinkle 32

14. Black sheep of the family 34

15. Kettle rag 36

1. TURKEY IN THE STRAW

Christopher Norton

più accel al fine

2. SWANEE RIVER

Christopher Norton

Slower to the end

3. POLLY WOLLY DOODLE

Christopher Norton

4. CARRY ME BACK

Christopher Norton

5. DIXIE

Christopher Norton

6. KING BOOGIE

Christopher Norton

7. We Wish

right
Christopher Norton

8. GOOD CHRISTIAN MEN

Christopher Norton

9. CAMEL STOMP

Christopher Norton

10. I saw three ships

Christopher Norton

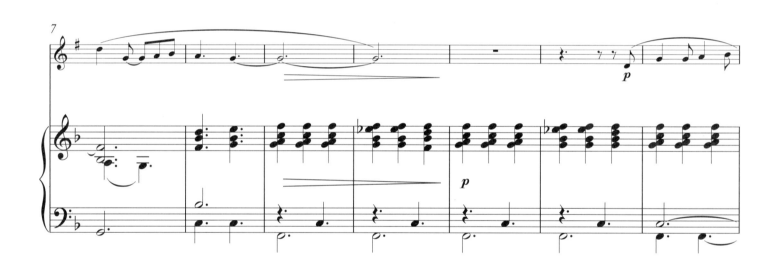

25

11. PUT IT ALL TOGETHER

Christopher Norton

12. Hush little baby

Christopher Norton

13. TWINKLE

Christopher Norton

14. BLACK SHEEP OF THE FAMILY

Christopher Norton

15. KETTLE RAG

Christopher Norton

9. CAMEL STOMP

Christopher Norton

10. I SAW THREE SHIPS

Christopher Norton

Slowing to the end

11. PUT IT ALL TOGETHER

Christopher Norton

12. HUSH LITTLE BABY

Christopher Norton

13. TWINKLE

Christopher Norton

BLANK

14. BLACK SHEEP OF THE FAMILY

Christopher Norton

15. KETTLE RAG

Christopher Norton

CHRISTOPHER NORTON'S

CONCERT COLLECTION

THE *Christopher Norton*
CONCERT COLLECTION
FOR **ALTO SAXOPHONE**

THE *Christopher Norton*
CONCERT COLLECTION
FOR **CLARINET**

Christopher Norton
CONCERT COLLECTION
FOR **FLUTE**

Christopher Norton
CONCERT COLLECTION
FOR **TRUMPET**

Christopher Norton
CONCERT COLLECTION
FOR **VIOLIN**

ISMN 979-0-060-11988-0

ISMN 979-0-060-11669-8

ISMN 979-0-060-11670-4

ISMN 979-0-060-11989-7

ISMN 979-0-060-11987-3

BOOSEY&HAWKES